Thank you for a drink of water

Patricia & Victor Smeltzer

A LION BOOK

Ben was thirsty,
so he had a drink of water.

"Thank you, **glass,**
for my drink of water,"
said Ben.

"Don't thank me,"
said the glass.
"I only held the water.
You must thank the one
who gave me the water."

So Ben went to say
"Thank you" to ...

... the **tap.**

"Thank you, **tap,**
   for my drink of water,"
said Ben.

"Don't thank me,"
   said the tap.
"I only let the water flow.
   You must thank the ones
   who gave me the water."

So Ben went to say
"Thank you" to ...

... the **water pipes.**

"Thank you, **water pipes,**
for my drink of water,"
said Ben.

"Don't thank us,"
said the water pipes.
"We only carried the water.
You must thank the one
who gave us the water."

So Ben went to say
"Thank you" to ...

... the **reservoir.**

"Thank you, **reservoir,**
for my drink of water,"
said Ben.

"Don't thank me,"
said the reservoir.
"I only stored the water.
You must thank the one
who gave me the water."

So Ben went to say
"Thank you" to ...

... the **river.**

"Thank you, **river,**
for my drink of water,"
said Ben.

"Don't thank me," said the river.
"I only brought the water.
You must thank the one
who gave me the water."

So Ben went to say
"Thank you" to ...

... the **rain.**

"Thank you, **rain,**
   for my drink of water,"
   said Ben.

"Don't thank me,"
   said the rain.
"I only fell from the sky!
   You must thank the one
   who carried me a long way."

So Ben went to say
"Thank you" to ...

... the **cloud.**

"Thank you, **cloud,**
   for my drink of water,"
   said Ben.

"Don't thank me,"
   said the cloud.
"I only held
   the tiny drops of water.
   You must thank the one
   who gave me the water."

So Ben went to say
"Thank you" to ...

... the **sea.**

"Thank you, **sea,**
for my drink of water,"
said Ben.

"Don't thank me," said the sea.
"You must thank the one
who made the mist
rise from me into the air."
The mist is made of
tiny drops of water
like those in the cloud.

So Ben went to say
"Thank you" to ...

... the **sun.**

"Thank you, **sun,**
for my drink of water,"
said Ben.

"Don't thank me,"
said the sun.
"You must thank the one
who made me."

So Ben said "Thank you" to ...

... **God.**

Ben said this prayer:

"Thank you, **God,**
for making the **sun,**

and the **sea,**

and the **cloud.**

Thank you, **God,**
for making the **rain,**

and the **river.**

Thank you, **God,**
for helping people
to make
the **reservoir,**

and the **water pipes,**

and the **tap,**

and the **glass.**

Thank you, **God,**
for my **drink of water.**

Amen."